The Black Girl's Guide to Emotional Healing Journal

Nijiama Smalls

Hey Sis,

Welcome back! I'm so glad you are embarking on the next step in your journey to healing. You are doing well and I'm so proud of you for making this important investment in to your emotional health. Not only is this step vital but it's continual as it well help you process your day-to-day experiences and the emotions attached to them.

Journaling is such a powerful tool with many health and wellness benefits. Not only does it help you manage stress, but it also helps improve your memory, gain a better understanding of yourself, clear your mind, achieve your goals, and release pent-up feelings.[1, 2]

In this guided journal, you will set and track monthly goals. You will reflect on your thoughts and emotions each day. At the end of the week and month, I'd like for you to take notice of any patterns that you see regarding your thoughts, feelings, and emotions. This will help you as you develop self-awareness, realize your triggers, and manage toxic thoughts.

Please note that this journal consists of five weeks in each month to account for the extra days in some of the months. You can choose how you wish to manage the days in the month.

Journal daily in a quiet space. Try to be as consistent as you can but be kind to yourself. It's OK if you miss a day. Consistency takes time.

Eventually, you will begin to notice the changes that you are making and the improvements to your emotional health. Remember to celebrate each change. Even the smallest change is worth celebrating.[2]

I want to truly encourage you to commit to doing this. Make this a part of your daily self-care routine because emotional care is vital to our overall well-being. When you invest in becoming emotionally whole, you open yourself to a world of new possibilities, experiences, and relationships. The time is now for us to control our emotions instead of allowing them to control us. The time is now for us to heal and pass it down to future generations.

ISBN 978-1-7346928-4-6

List of Emotions

Please use this list as you answer the daily and weekly questions

Anger
Amazed
Annoyed
Anxious
Ashamed
Bitter
Bored
Comfortable
Confused
Content
Depressed
Desperate
Determined
Disdain
Disgusted
Eager
Embarrassed
Energetic
Envious
Foolish
Frustrated
Furious
Grieving
Happy
Hopeful
Hurt
Inadequate
Insecure
Inspired
Irritated
Jealous
Joy
Lonely
Lost
Loving
Miserable
Motivated
Nervous
Overwhelmed
Peaceful
Proud
Relieved
Resentful
Sad
Satisfied
Scared
Self-Conscious
Shame
Shocked
Silly
Stupid
Suspicious
Tense
Terrified
Trapped
Uncomfortable
Worried
Worthless
Valued

Monthly Goals

Financial goals for the month

Emotional goals for the month

Healthy eating goals for the month

Professional goals for the month

Exercise goals for the month

Prayer requests for the month

Day 1

Date: ______________________

The emotions that I experienced today are:

____

Things that caused me to feel this way:

____
____
____
____

Specifically, what thoughts did I have that led to me experiencing these emotions?

____
____
____
____

For the negative emotions, what thoughts or behaviors should I change or eliminate so that I will not feel these emotions when I have another experience similar to this:

____
____
____
____

What am I grateful for today?

____
____
____
____
____

Who/What made me laugh today?

____

Who showed me kindness today?

____

What did they do to demonstrate kindness to me?

____

____

____

____

Date: ______________________________

Journal Entry (here is where can you discuss anything you'd like):

Day 2 Date: ______________________________

The emotions that I experienced today are:

____

Things that caused me to feel this way:

____

____

____

____

Specifically, what thoughts did I have that led to me experiencing these emotions?

____

____

____

____

For the negative emotions, what thoughts or behaviors should I change or eliminate so that I will not feel these emotions when I have another experience similar to this:

____

____

____

____

What am I grateful for today?

____

____

____

____

Who/What made me laugh today?

____

Who showed me kindness today?

____

What did they do to demonstrate kindness to me?

Date: ____

Journal Entry (here is where can you discuss anything you'd like):

Day 3 Date: ______________________________

The emotions that I experienced today are:

____

Things that caused me to feel this way:

____

____

____

____

Specifically, what thoughts did I have that led to me experiencing these emotions?

____

____

____

____

For the negative emotions, what thoughts or behaviors should I change or eliminate so that I will not feel these emotions when I have another experience similar to this:

____

____

____

____

What am I grateful for today?

____

____

____

____

Who/What made me laugh today?

____

Who showed me kindness today?

____

What did they do to demonstrate kindness to me?

____

____

____

____

Date: ____

Journal Entry (here is where can you discuss anything you'd like):

Day 4

Date: ______________________________

The emotions that I experienced today are:

____

Things that caused me to feel this way:

____
____
____
____

Specifically, what thoughts did I have that led to me experiencing these emotions?

____
____
____
____

For the negative emotions, what thoughts or behaviors should I change or eliminate so that I will not feel these emotions when I have another experience similar to this:

____
____
____
____

What am I grateful for today?

____
____
____
____

Who/What made me laugh today?

____

Who showed me kindness today?

____

What did they do to demonstrate kindness to me?

____

____

____

____

Date: ______________________________

Journal Entry (here is where can you discuss anything you'd like):

Day 5 Date: ____________________

The emotions that I experienced today are:

____

Things that caused me to feel this way:

____
____
____
____

Specifically, what thoughts did I have that led to me experiencing these emotions?

____
____
____
____

For the negative emotions, what thoughts or behaviors should I change or eliminate so that I will not feel these emotions when I have another experience similar to this:

____
____
____
____

What am I grateful for today?

____
____
____
____

Who/What made me laugh today?

____

Who showed me kindness today?

____

What did they do to demonstrate kindness to me?

____

____

____

____

Date: ______________________________

Journal Entry (here is where can you discuss anything you'd like):

Day 6 Date: ______________________

The emotions that I experienced today are:

____

Things that caused me to feel this way:

____

____

____

____

Specifically, what thoughts did I have that led to me experiencing these emotions?

____

____

____

____

For the negative emotions, what thoughts or behaviors should I change or eliminate so that I will not feel these emotions when I have another experience similar to this:

____

____

____

____

What am I grateful for today?

____

____

____

____

Who/What made me laugh today?

____

Who showed me kindness today?

____

What did they do to demonstrate kindness to me?

____

____

____

____

Date: ______________________________

Journal Entry (here is where can you discuss anything you'd like):

Day 7 Date: ____

The emotions that I experienced today are:

____

Things that caused me to feel this way:

____

____

____

____

Specifically, what thoughts did I have that led to me experiencing these emotions?

____

____

____

____

For the negative emotions, what thoughts or behaviors should I change or eliminate so that I will not feel these emotions when I have another experience similar to this:

____

____

____

____

What am I grateful for today?

____

____

____

____

Who/What made me laugh today?

____

Who showed me kindness today?

____

What did they do to demonstrate kindness to me?

____

____

____

____

Date: ____

Journal Entry (here is where can you discuss anything you'd like):

Snapshot of My Week

Check all of the positive traits that you demonstrated this week

Leadership
Kindness
Love
Loyalty
Humility
Compassion
Self-Compassion
Flexibility
Confidence
Teachable
Courage
Focus
Open Communication
Understanding
Selflessness
Authenticity
Fearlessness
Assertiveness
Self-Control
Forgiveness

Check all of the negative traits that you demonstrated this week

Anger
Malice
Judgement
Abrasive
Jealousy
Self-destructive
Envy
Stubborn
Rudeness
Gossip
Fear
Defensiveness
Deceit
Selfishness
Gullible
Manipulative

Best moment of the week

Worst moment of the week

Did I stay in control of my emotions this week? How so?

Lessons learned

What do I need to change?

What can't I change?

How can I move towards accepting what I can't change?

Day 8

Date:____________________________

The emotions that I experienced today are:

Things that caused me to feel this way:

Specifically, what thoughts did I have that led to me experiencing these emotions?

For the negative emotions, what thoughts or behaviors should I change or eliminate so that I will not feel these emotions when I have another experience similar to this:

What am I grateful for today?

Who/What made me laugh today?

Who showed me kindness today?

What did they do to demonstrate kindness to me?

____

____

____

____

Date: ____

Journal Entry (here is where can you discuss anything you'd like):

____
____
____
____
____
____
____
____
____
____
____
____
____
____
____
____
____
____
____
____
____
____
____
____
____
____
____
____
____
____
____
____
____
____

Day 9

Date: ______________________________

The emotions that I experienced today are:

____

Things that caused me to feel this way:

____
____
____
____

Specifically, what thoughts did I have that led to me experiencing these emotions?

____
____
____
____

For the negative emotions, what thoughts or behaviors should I change or eliminate so that I will not feel these emotions when I have another experience similar to this:

____
____
____
____

What am I grateful for today?

____
____
____
____

Who/What made me laugh today?

____

Who showed me kindness today?

____

What did they do to demonstrate kindness to me?

____

____

____

____

Date: ______________________________

Journal Entry (here is where can you discuss anything you'd like):

Day 10 Date: ______________________

The emotions that I experienced today are:

____

Things that caused me to feel this way:

____

____

____

____

Specifically, what thoughts did I have that led to me experiencing these emotions?

____

____

____

____

For the negative emotions, what thoughts or behaviors should I change or eliminate so that I will not feel these emotions when I have another experience similar to this:

____

____

____

____

What am I grateful for today?

____

____

____

____

Who/What made me laugh today?

____

Who showed me kindness today?

____

What did they do to demonstrate kindness to me?

____

____

____

____

Date: ____

Journal Entry (here is where can you discuss anything you'd like):

Day 11 Date: ______________________________

The emotions that I experienced today are:

____

Things that caused me to feel this way:

____

____

____

____

Specifically, what thoughts did I have that led to me experiencing these emotions?

____

____

____

____

For the negative emotions, what thoughts or behaviors should I change or eliminate so that I will not feel these emotions when I have another experience similar to this:

____

____

____

____

What am I grateful for today?

____

____

____

____

Who/What made me laugh today?

____

Who showed me kindness today?

____

What did they do to demonstrate kindness to me?

____

____

____

____

Date: ____

Journal Entry (here is where can you discuss anything you'd like):

Day 12

Date: ______________________________

The emotions that I experienced today are:

____

Things that caused me to feel this way:

____

____

____

____

Specifically, what thoughts did I have that led to me experiencing these emotions?

____

____

____

____

For the negative emotions, what thoughts or behaviors should I change or eliminate so that I will not feel these emotions when I have another experience similar to this:

____

____

____

____

What am I grateful for today?

____

____

____

____

Who/What made me laugh today?

____

Who showed me kindness today?

____

What did they do to demonstrate kindness to me?

____

____

____

____

Date: ____

Journal Entry (here is where can you discuss anything you'd like):

Day 13

Date: ______________________

The emotions that I experienced today are:

____

Things that caused me to feel this way:

____

____

____

____

Specifically, what thoughts did I have that led to me experiencing these emotions?

____

____

____

____

For the negative emotions, what thoughts or behaviors should I change or eliminate so that I will not feel these emotions when I have another experience similar to this:

____

____

____

____

What am I grateful for today?

____

____

____

____

Who/What made me laugh today?

____

Who showed me kindness today?

____

What did they do to demonstrate kindness to me?

____

____

____

____

Date: ______________________________

Journal Entry (here is where can you discuss anything you'd like):

Day 14 Date: ____________________

The emotions that I experienced today are:

____

Things that caused me to feel this way:

____

____

____

____

Specifically, what thoughts did I have that led to me experiencing these emotions?

____

____

____

____

For the negative emotions, what thoughts or behaviors should I change or eliminate so that I will not feel these emotions when I have another experience similar to this:

____

____

____

____

What am I grateful for today?

____

____

____

____

Who/What made me laugh today?

____

Who showed me kindness today?

____

What did they do to demonstrate kindness to me?

____

____

____

____

Date: ____

Journal Entry (here is where can you discuss anything you'd like):

____
____
____
____
____
____
____
____
____
____
____
____
____
____
____
____
____
____
____
____
____
____
____
____
____
____
____
____
____
____
____
____
____

Snapshot of My Week

Check all of the positive traits that you demonstrated this week

Leadership
Kindness
Love
Loyalty
Humility
Compassion
Self-Compassion
Flexibility
Confidence
Teachable
Courage
Focus
Open Communication
Understanding
Selflessness
Authenticity
Fearlessness
Assertiveness
Self-Control
Forgiveness

Check all of the negative traits that you demonstrated this week

Anger
Malice
Judgement
Abrasive
Jealousy
Self-destructive
Envy
Stubborn
Rudeness
Gossip
Fear
Defensiveness
Deceit
Selfishness
Gullible
Manipulative

Best moment of the week

Worst moment of the week

Did I stay in control of my emotions this week?

Lessons learned

What do I need to change?

What can't I change?

How can I move towards accepting what I can't change?

Day 15

Date: ______________________________

The emotions that I experienced today are:

____

Things that caused me to feel this way:

____

____

____

____

____

Specifically, what thoughts did I have that led to me experiencing these emotions?

____

____

____

____

____

For the negative emotions, what thoughts or behaviors should I change or eliminate so that I will not feel these emotions when I have another experience similar to this:

____

____

____

____

What am I grateful for today?

____

____

____

____

Who/What made me laugh today?

____

Who showed me kindness today?

____

What did they do to demonstrate kindness to me?

___

___

___

___

Date: ____________________

Journal Entry (here is where can you discuss anything you'd like):

Day 16 Date: ____________________

The emotions that I experienced today are:

____

Things that caused me to feel this way:

____

____

____

____

Specifically, what thoughts did I have that led to me experiencing these emotions?

____

____

____

____

For the negative emotions, what thoughts or behaviors should I change or eliminate so that I will not feel these emotions when I have another experience similar to this:

____

____

____

What am I grateful for today?

____

____

____

____

____

Who/What made me laugh today?

____

Who showed me kindness today?

____

What did they do to demonstrate kindness to me?

____

____

____

____

Date: ______________________________

Journal Entry (here is where can you discuss anything you'd like):

Day 17

Date: ______________________________

The emotions that I experienced today are:

____

Things that caused me to feel this way:

____

____

____

____

Specifically, what thoughts did I have that led to me experiencing these emotions?

____

____

____

____

For the negative emotions, what thoughts or behaviors should I change or eliminate so that I will not feel these emotions when I have another experience similar to this:

____

____

____

____

What am I grateful for today?

____

____

____

____

Who/What made me laugh today?

____

Who showed me kindness today?

____

What did they do to demonstrate kindness to me?

____

____

____

____

Date: ____

Journal Entry (here is where can you discuss anything you'd like):

Day 18 Date: ____________________

The emotions that I experienced today are:

____

Things that caused me to feel this way:

____

____

____

____

____

Specifically, what thoughts did I have that led to me experiencing these emotions?

____

____

____

____

For the negative emotions, what thoughts or behaviors should I change or eliminate so that I will not feel these emotions when I have another experience similar to this:

____

____

____

____

What am I grateful for today?

____

____

____

____

Who/What made me laugh today?

____

Who showed me kindness today?

____

What did they do to demonstrate kindness to me?

___

___

___

___

Date: ____________________

Journal Entry (here is where can you discuss anything you'd like):

Day 19 Date: ____________________

The emotions that I experienced today are:

____

Things that caused me to feel this way:

____

____

____

____

Specifically, what thoughts did I have that led to me experiencing these emotions?

____

____

____

____

For the negative emotions, what thoughts or behaviors should I change or eliminate so that I will not feel these emotions when I have another experience similar to this:

____

____

____

____

What am I grateful for today?

____

____

____

____

Who/What made me laugh today?

____

Who showed me kindness today?

____

What did they do to demonstrate kindness to me?

____

____

____

____

Date: ______________________________

Journal Entry (here is where can you discuss anything you'd like):

Day 20

Date: ______________________________

The emotions that I experienced today are:

____

Things that caused me to feel this way:

____

____

____

____

Specifically, what thoughts did I have that led to me experiencing these emotions?

____

____

____

____

For the negative emotions, what thoughts or behaviors should I change or eliminate so that I will not feel these emotions when I have another experience similar to this:

____

____

____

____

What am I grateful for today?

____

____

____

____

Who/What made me laugh today?

____

Who showed me kindness today?

____

What did they do to demonstrate kindness to me?

____

____

____

____

Date: ____

Journal Entry (here is where can you discuss anything you'd like):

Day 21

Date: ______________________________

The emotions that I experienced today are:

____

Things that caused me to feel this way:

____
____
____
____
____

Specifically, what thoughts did I have that led to me experiencing these emotions?

____
____
____
____
____

For the negative emotions, what thoughts or behaviors should I change or eliminate so that I will not feel these emotions when I have another experience similar to this:

____
____
____
____

What am I grateful for today?

____
____
____
____

Who/What made me laugh today?

____

Who showed me kindness today?

____

What did they do to demonstrate kindness to me?

___

___

___

___

Date: ____

Journal Entry (here is where can you discuss anything you'd like):

Snapshot of My Week

Check all of the positive traits that you demonstrated this week

Leadership
Kindness
Love
Loyalty
Humility
Compassion
Self-Compassion
Flexibility
Confidence
Teachable
Courage
Focus
Open Communication
Understanding
Selflessness
Authenticity
Fearlessness
Assertiveness
Self-Control
Forgiveness

Check all of the negative traits that you demonstrated this week

Anger
Malice
Judgement
Abrasive
Jealousy
Self-destructive
Envy
Stubborn
Rudeness
Gossip
Fear
Defensiveness
Deceit
Selfishness
Gullible
Manipulative

Best moment of the week

Worst moment of the week

Did I stay in control of my emotions this week?

Lessons learned

What do I need to change?

What can't I change?

How can I move towards accepting what I can't change?

Day 22 Date: ____________________

The emotions that I experienced today are:

____

Things that caused me to feel this way:

____

____

____

____

Specifically, what thoughts did I have that led to me experiencing these emotions?

____

____

____

____

For the negative emotions, what thoughts or behaviors should I change or eliminate so that I will not feel these emotions when I have another experience similar to this:

____

____

____

____

What am I grateful for today?

____

____

____

____

Who/What made me laugh today?

____

Who showed me kindness today?

____

What did they do to demonstrate kindness to me?

___

___

___

___

Date: ____

Journal Entry (here is where can you discuss anything you'd like):

Day 23

Date: ______________________________

The emotions that I experienced today are:

____

Things that caused me to feel this way:

____
____
____
____

Specifically, what thoughts did I have that led to me experiencing these emotions?

____
____
____
____

For the negative emotions, what thoughts or behaviors should I change or eliminate so that I will not feel these emotions when I have another experience similar to this:

____
____
____
____

What am I grateful for today?

____
____
____
____

Who/What made me laugh today?

____

Who showed me kindness today?

____

What did they do to demonstrate kindness to me?

____

____

____

____

Date: ____

Journal Entry (here is where can you discuss anything you'd like):

Day 24 Date: ______________________________

The emotions that I experienced today are:

____

Things that caused me to feel this way:

____

____

____

____

Specifically, what thoughts did I have that led to me experiencing these emotions?

____

____

____

____

For the negative emotions, what thoughts or behaviors should I change or eliminate so that I will not feel these emotions when I have another experience similar to this:

____

____

____

____

What am I grateful for today?

____

____

____

____

Who/What made me laugh today?

____

Who showed me kindness today?

____

What did they do to demonstrate kindness to me?

____

____

____

____

Date: ____

Journal Entry (here is where can you discuss anything you'd like):

Day 25 Date: ______________________________

The emotions that I experienced today are:

____

Things that caused me to feel this way:

____

____

____

____

Specifically, what thoughts did I have that led to me experiencing these emotions?

____

____

____

____

For the negative emotions, what thoughts or behaviors should I change or eliminate so that I will not feel these emotions when I have another experience similar to this:

____

____

____

____

What am I grateful for today?

____

____

____

____

Who/What made me laugh today?

____

Who showed me kindness today?

____

What did they do to demonstrate kindness to me?

____

____

____

____

Date: ____

Journal Entry (here is where can you discuss anything you'd like):

Day 26 Date: ______________________________

The emotions that I experienced today are:

____

Things that caused me to feel this way:

____
____
____
____

Specifically, what thoughts did I have that led to me experiencing these emotions?

____
____
____
____

For the negative emotions, what thoughts or behaviors should I change or eliminate so that I will not feel these emotions when I have another experience similar to this:

____
____
____
____

What am I grateful for today?

____
____
____
____

Who/What made me laugh today?

____

Who showed me kindness today?

____

What did they do to demonstrate kindness to me?

____

____

____

____

Date: ______________________________

Journal Entry (here is where can you discuss anything you'd like):

Day 27 Date: ______________________

The emotions that I experienced today are:

____

Things that caused me to feel this way:

____

____

____

____

Specifically, what thoughts did I have that led to me experiencing these emotions?

____

____

____

____

For the negative emotions, what thoughts or behaviors should I change or eliminate so that I will not feel these emotions when I have another experience similar to this:

____

____

____

____

What am I grateful for today?

____

____

____

____

Who/What made me laugh today?

____

Who showed me kindness today?

____

What did they do to demonstrate kindness to me?

____

____

____

____

Date: ____

Journal Entry (here is where can you discuss anything you'd like):

Day 28 Date: ____________________

The emotions that I experienced today are:

____

Things that caused me to feel this way:

____

____

____

____

Specifically, what thoughts did I have that led to me experiencing these emotions?

____

____

____

____

For the negative emotions, what thoughts or behaviors should I change or eliminate so that I will not feel these emotions when I have another experience similar to this:

____

____

____

____

What am I grateful for today?

____

____

____

____

Who/What made me laugh today?

____

Who showed me kindness today?

____

What did they do to demonstrate kindness to me?

____

____

____

____

Date: ____

Journal Entry (here is where can you discuss anything you'd like):

Snapshot of My Week

Check all of the positive traits that you demonstrated this week

Leadership
Kindness
Love
Loyalty
Humility
Compassion
Self-Compassion
Flexibility
Confidence
Teachable
Courage
Focus
Open Communication
Understanding
Selflessness
Authenticity
Fearlessness
Assertiveness
Self-Control
Forgiveness

Check all of the negative traits that you demonstrated this week

Anger
Malice
Judgement
Abrasive
Jealousy
Self-destructive
Envy
Stubborn
Rudeness
Gossip
Fear
Defensiveness
Deceit
Selfishness
Gullible
Manipulative

Best moment of the week

Worst moment of the week

Did I stay in control of my emotions this week?

Lessons learned

What do I need to change?

What can't I change?

How can I move towards accepting what I can't change?

Day 29 Date: ______________________

The emotions that I experienced today are:

____

Things that caused me to feel this way:

____

____

____

____

Specifically, what thoughts did I have that led to me experiencing these emotions?

____

____

____

____

For the negative emotions, what thoughts or behaviors should I change or eliminate so that I will not feel these emotions when I have another experience similar to this:

____

____

____

____

What am I grateful for today?

____

____

____

____

Who/What made me laugh today?

____

Who showed me kindness today?

____

What did they do to demonstrate kindness to me?

____

____

____

____

Date: ____

Journal Entry (here is where can you discuss anything you'd like):

Day 30 Date: ______________________

The emotions that I experienced today are:

____

Things that caused me to feel this way:

____
____
____
____

Specifically, what thoughts did I have that led to me experiencing these emotions?

____
____
____
____

For the negative emotions, what thoughts or behaviors should I change or eliminate so that I will not feel these emotions when I have another experience similar to this:

____
____
____
____

What am I grateful for today?

____
____
____
____

Who/What made me laugh today?

____

Who showed me kindness today?

____

What did they do to demonstrate kindness to me?

____

____

____

____

Date: ____

Journal Entry (here is where can you discuss anything you'd like):

Day 31

Date: ______________________

The emotions that I experienced today are:

Things that caused me to feel this way:

Specifically, what thoughts did I have that led to me experiencing these emotions?

For the negative emotions, what thoughts or behaviors should I change or eliminate so that I will not feel these emotions when I have another experience similar to this:

What am I grateful for today?

Who/What made me laugh today?

Who showed me kindness today?

What did they do to demonstrate kindness to me?

____

____

____

____

Date: ____

Journal Entry (here is where can you discuss anything you'd like):

Day 32 Date: ______________________________

The emotions that I experienced today are:

____

Things that caused me to feel this way:

____
____
____
____

Specifically, what thoughts did I have that led to me experiencing these emotions?

____
____
____
____

For the negative emotions, what thoughts or behaviors should I change or eliminate so that I will not feel these emotions when I have another experience similar to this:

____
____
____
____

What am I grateful for today?

____
____
____
____

Who/What made me laugh today?

____

Who showed me kindness today?

____

What did they do to demonstrate kindness to me?

___

___

___

___

Date: ____

Journal Entry (here is where can you discuss anything you'd like):

Day 33 Date: ___________________________

The emotions that I experienced today are:

____

Things that caused me to feel this way:

____

____

____

____

Specifically, what thoughts did I have that led to me experiencing these emotions?

____

____

____

____

For the negative emotions, what thoughts or behaviors should I change or eliminate so that I will not feel these emotions when I have another experience similar to this:

____

____

____

____

What am I grateful for today?

____

____

____

____

Who/What made me laugh today?

____

Who showed me kindness today?

____

What did they do to demonstrate kindness to me?

____

____

____

____

Date: ____

Journal Entry (here is where can you discuss anything you'd like):

Day 34 Date: ______________________

The emotions that I experienced today are:

____

Things that caused me to feel this way:

____
____
____
____

Specifically, what thoughts did I have that led to me experiencing these emotions?

____
____
____
____

For the negative emotions, what thoughts or behaviors should I change or eliminate so that I will not feel these emotions when I have another experience similar to this:

____
____
____
____

What am I grateful for today?

____
____
____
____

Who/What made me laugh today?

____

Who showed me kindness today?

____

What did they do to demonstrate kindness to me?

____

____

____

____

Date: ____

Journal Entry (here is where can you discuss anything you'd like):

Day 35 Date: ______________________________

The emotions that I experienced today are:

____

Things that caused me to feel this way:

____

____

____

____

Specifically, what thoughts did I have that led to me experiencing these emotions?

____

____

____

____

For the negative emotions, what thoughts or behaviors should I change or eliminate so that I will not feel these emotions when I have another experience similar to this:

____

____

____

____

What am I grateful for today?

____

____

____

____

Who/What made me laugh today?

____

Who showed me kindness today?

____

What did they do to demonstrate kindness to me?

____

____

____

____

Date: ____

Journal Entry (here is where can you discuss anything you'd like):

Snapshot of My Week

Check all of the positive traits that you demonstrated this week

Leadership
Kindness
Love
Loyalty
Humility
Compassion
Self-Compassion
Flexibility
Confidence
Teachable
Courage

Focus
Open Communication
Understanding
Selflessness
Authenticity
Fearlessness
Assertiveness
Self-Control
Forgiveness

Check all of the negative traits that you demonstrated this week

Anger
Malice
Judgement
Abrasive
Jealousy
Self-destructive

Envy
Stubborn
Rudeness
Gossip
Fear

Defensiveness
Deceit
Selfishness
Gullible
Manipulative

Best moment of the week

Worst moment of the week

Did I stay in control of my emotions this week?

Lessons learned

What do I need to change?

What can't I change?

How can I move towards accepting what I can't change?

Monthly Goals Achieved

Monthly financial goals achieved

____
____
____
____
____
____

Monthly emotional goals achieved

____
____
____
____
____
____

Monthly nutrition goals achieved

____
____
____
____
____
____

Monthly professional goals achieved

____
____
____
____
____
____

Monthly exercise goals achieved

____
____
____
____
____
____

Monthly prayers answered

____
____
____
____
____
____
____

Do you overreact? If yes, which triggers cause you to overreact?

____

____

____

____

____

____

____

Monthly Goals

Healthy eating goals for the month

Professional goals for the month

Financial goals for the month

Emotional goals for the month

Exercise goals for the month

Prayer requests for the month

Day 36 Date: ______________________

The emotions that I experienced today are:

____

Things that caused me to feel this way:

____

____

____

____

Specifically, what thoughts did I have that led to me experiencing these emotions?

____

____

____

____

For the negative emotions, what thoughts or behaviors should I change or eliminate so that I will not feel these emotions when I have another experience similar to this:

____

____

____

____

What am I grateful for today?

____

____

____

____

____

Who/What made me laugh today?

____

Who showed me kindness today?

____

What did they do to demonstrate kindness to me?

____

____

____

____

Date: ______________________________

Journal Entry (here is where can you discuss anything you'd like):

Day 37 Date: ______________________

The emotions that I experienced today are:

____

Things that caused me to feel this way:

____

____

____

____

Specifically, what thoughts did I have that led to me experiencing these emotions?

____

____

____

____

For the negative emotions, what thoughts or behaviors should I change or eliminate so that I will not feel these emotions when I have another experience similar to this:

____

____

____

____

What am I grateful for today?

____

____

____

____

Who/What made me laugh today?

____

Who showed me kindness today?

____

What did they do to demonstrate kindness to me?

____

____

____

____

Date: ____

Journal Entry (here is where can you discuss anything you'd like):

Day 38 Date: ______________________________

The emotions that I experienced today are:

____

Things that caused me to feel this way:

____
____
____
____

Specifically, what thoughts did I have that led to me experiencing these emotions?

____
____
____
____

For the negative emotions, what thoughts or behaviors should I change or eliminate so that I will not feel these emotions when I have another experience similar to this:

____
____
____
____

What am I grateful for today?

____
____
____
____

Who/What made me laugh today?

____

Who showed me kindness today?

____

What did they do to demonstrate kindness to me?

____

____

____

____

Date: ____

Journal Entry (here is where can you discuss anything you'd like):

Day 39 Date: ______________________________

The emotions that I experienced today are:

____

Things that caused me to feel this way:

____
____
____
____

Specifically, what thoughts did I have that led to me experiencing these emotions?

____
____
____
____

For the negative emotions, what thoughts or behaviors should I change or eliminate so that I will not feel these emotions when I have another experience similar to this:

____
____
____
____

What am I grateful for today?

____
____
____
____

Who/What made me laugh today?

____

Who showed me kindness today?

____

What did they do to demonstrate kindness to me?

Date: ______________________________________

Journal Entry (here is where can you discuss anything you'd like):

Day 40 Date: ______________________________

The emotions that I experienced today are:

____

Things that caused me to feel this way:

____
____
____
____

Specifically, what thoughts did I have that led to me experiencing these emotions?

____
____
____
____

For the negative emotions, what thoughts or behaviors should I change or eliminate so that I will not feel these emotions when I have another experience similar to this:

____
____
____
____

What am I grateful for today?

____
____
____
____

Who/What made me laugh today?

____

Who showed me kindness today?

____

What did they do to demonstrate kindness to me?

___

___

___

___

Date: ______________________________

Journal Entry (here is where can you discuss anything you'd like):

Day 41

Date: ______________________________

The emotions that I experienced today are:

____

Things that caused me to feel this way:

____

____

____

____

Specifically, what thoughts did I have that led to me experiencing these emotions?

____

____

____

____

For the negative emotions, what thoughts or behaviors should I change or eliminate so that I will not feel these emotions when I have another experience similar to this:

____

____

____

____

What am I grateful for today?

____

____

____

____

Who/What made me laugh today?

____

Who showed me kindness today?

____

What did they do to demonstrate kindness to me?

Date: ____________________

Journal Entry (here is where can you discuss anything you'd like):

Day 42 Date: ______________________

The emotions that I experienced today are:

____

Things that caused me to feel this way:

____
____
____
____

Specifically, what thoughts did I have that led to me experiencing these emotions?

____
____
____
____

For the negative emotions, what thoughts or behaviors should I change or eliminate so that I will not feel these emotions when I have another experience similar to this:

____
____
____
____

What am I grateful for today?

____
____
____
____

Who/What made me laugh today?

____

Who showed me kindness today?

____

What did they do to demonstrate kindness to me?

____

____

____

____

Date: ____

Journal Entry (here is where can you discuss anything you'd like):

____
____
____
____
____
____
____
____
____
____
____
____
____
____
____
____
____
____
____
____
____
____
____
____
____
____
____
____
____
____
____
____
____
____

Snapshot of My Week

Check all of the positive traits that you demonstrated this week

- Leadership
- Kindness
- Love
- Loyalty
- Humility
- Compassion
- Self-Compassion
- Flexibility
- Confidence
- Teachable
- Courage
- Focus
- Open Communication
- Understanding
- Selflessness
- Authenticity
- Fearlessness
- Assertiveness
- Self-Control
- Forgiveness

Check all of the negative traits that you demonstrated this week

- Anger
- Malice
- Judgement
- Abrasive
- Jealousy
- Self-destructive
- Envy
- Stubborn
- Rudeness
- Gossip
- Fear
- Defensiveness
- Deceit
- Selfishness
- Gullible
- Manipulative

Best moment of the week

Worst moment of the week

Did I stay in control of my emotions this week? How so?

Lessons learned

What do I need to change?

What can't I change?

How can I move towards accepting what I can't change?

Day 43 Date: ______________________________

The emotions that I experienced today are:

____

Things that caused me to feel this way:

____
____
____
____

Specifically, what thoughts did I have that led to me experiencing these emotions?

____
____
____
____

For the negative emotions, what thoughts or behaviors should I change or eliminate so that I will not feel these emotions when I have another experience similar to this:

____
____
____
____

What am I grateful for today?

____
____
____
____

Who/What made me laugh today?

____

Who showed me kindness today?

____

What did they do to demonstrate kindness to me?

____

____

____

____

Date: ____

Journal Entry (here is where can you discuss anything you'd like):

Day 44 Date: ______________________________

The emotions that I experienced today are:

____

Things that caused me to feel this way:

____
____
____
____

Specifically, what thoughts did I have that led to me experiencing these emotions?

____
____
____
____

For the negative emotions, what thoughts or behaviors should I change or eliminate so that I will not feel these emotions when I have another experience similar to this:

____
____
____
____

What am I grateful for today?

____
____
____
____

Who/What made me laugh today?

____

Who showed me kindness today?

____

What did they do to demonstrate kindness to me?

____

____

____

____

Date: ____

Journal Entry (here is where can you discuss anything you'd like):

Day 45 Date: ____________________

The emotions that I experienced today are:

___

Things that caused me to feel this way:

___

___

___

___

Specifically, what thoughts did I have that led to me experiencing these emotions?

___

___

___

___

For the negative emotions, what thoughts or behaviors should I change or eliminate so that I will not feel these emotions when I have another experience similar to this:

___

___

___

___

What am I grateful for today?

___

___

___

___

Who/What made me laugh today?

___

Who showed me kindness today?

___

What did they do to demonstrate kindness to me?

____

____

____

____

Date: ______________________________

Journal Entry (here is where can you discuss anything you'd like):

Day 46 Date: ____________________

The emotions that I experienced today are:

____

Things that caused me to feel this way:

____
____
____
____

Specifically, what thoughts did I have that led to me experiencing these emotions?

____
____
____
____

For the negative emotions, what thoughts or behaviors should I change or eliminate so that I will not feel these emotions when I have another experience similar to this:

____
____
____
____

What am I grateful for today?

____
____
____
____

Who/What made me laugh today?

____

Who showed me kindness today?

____

What did they do to demonstrate kindness to me?

____

____

____

____

Date: ____

Journal Entry (here is where can you discuss anything you'd like):

Day 47

Date: ______________________________

The emotions that I experienced today are:

____

Things that caused me to feel this way:

____
____
____
____

Specifically, what thoughts did I have that led to me experiencing these emotions?

____
____
____
____

For the negative emotions, what thoughts or behaviors should I change or eliminate so that I will not feel these emotions when I have another experience similar to this:

____
____
____
____

What am I grateful for today?

____
____
____
____

Who/What made me laugh today?

____

Who showed me kindness today?

____

What did they do to demonstrate kindness to me?

____

____

____

____

Date: ____

Journal Entry (here is where can you discuss anything you'd like):

Day 48 Date: ______________________

The emotions that I experienced today are:

____

Things that caused me to feel this way:

____
____
____
____

Specifically, what thoughts did I have that led to me experiencing these emotions?

____
____
____
____

For the negative emotions, what thoughts or behaviors should I change or eliminate so that I will not feel these emotions when I have another experience similar to this:

____
____
____
____

What am I grateful for today?

____
____
____
____

Who/What made me laugh today?

____

Who showed me kindness today?

____

What did they do to demonstrate kindness to me?

Date: ______________________________

Journal Entry (here is where can you discuss anything you'd like):

Day 49 Date: ______________________________

The emotions that I experienced today are:

____

Things that caused me to feel this way:

____

____

____

____

Specifically, what thoughts did I have that led to me experiencing these emotions?

____

____

____

____

For the negative emotions, what thoughts or behaviors should I change or eliminate so that I will not feel these emotions when I have another experience similar to this:

____

____

____

____

What am I grateful for today?

____

____

____

____

Who/What made me laugh today?

____

Who showed me kindness today?

____

What did they do to demonstrate kindness to me?

____

____

____

____

Date: ______________________________________

Journal Entry (here is where can you discuss anything you'd like):

Snapshot of My Week

Check all of the positive traits that you demonstrated this week

Leadership
Kindness
Love
Loyalty
Humility
Compassion
Self-Compassion
Flexibility
Confidence
Teachable
Courage
Focus
Open Communication
Understanding
Selflessness
Authenticity
Fearlessness
Assertiveness
Self-Control
Forgiveness

Check all of the negative traits that you demonstrated this week

Anger
Malice
Judgement
Abrasive
Jealousy
Self-destructive
Envy
Stubborn
Rudeness
Gossip
Fear
Defensiveness
Deceit
Selfishness
Gullible
Manipulative

Best moment of the week

Worst moment of the week

Did I stay in control of my emotions this week?

Lessons learned

What do I need to change?

What can't I change?

How can I move towards accepting what I can't change?

Day 50 Date: ______________________________

The emotions that I experienced today are:

____

Things that caused me to feel this way:

____

____

____

____

____

Specifically, what thoughts did I have that led to me experiencing these emotions?

____

____

____

____

____

For the negative emotions, what thoughts or behaviors should I change or eliminate so that I will not feel these emotions when I have another experience similar to this:

____

____

____

____

What am I grateful for today?

____

____

____

____

Who/What made me laugh today?

____

Who showed me kindness today?

____

What did they do to demonstrate kindness to me?

____

____

____

____

Date: ____

Journal Entry (here is where can you discuss anything you'd like):

Day 51 Date: ______________________

The emotions that I experienced today are:

____

Things that caused me to feel this way:

____
____
____
____

Specifically, what thoughts did I have that led to me experiencing these emotions?

____
____
____
____

For the negative emotions, what thoughts or behaviors should I change or eliminate so that I will not feel these emotions when I have another experience similar to this:

____
____
____
____

What am I grateful for today?

____
____
____
____
____

Who/What made me laugh today?

____

Who showed me kindness today?

____

What did they do to demonstrate kindness to me?

____

____

____

____

Date: ________________________________

Journal Entry (here is where can you discuss anything you'd like):

Day 52 Date: ______________________

The emotions that I experienced today are:

____

Things that caused me to feel this way:

____

____

____

____

Specifically, what thoughts did I have that led to me experiencing these emotions?

____

____

____

____

For the negative emotions, what thoughts or behaviors should I change or eliminate so that I will not feel these emotions when I have another experience similar to this:

____

____

____

____

What am I grateful for today?

____

____

____

____

Who/What made me laugh today?

____

Who showed me kindness today?

____

What did they do to demonstrate kindness to me?

___

___

___

___

Date: ______________________________

Journal Entry (here is where can you discuss anything you'd like):

Day 53 Date: ______________________

The emotions that I experienced today are:

____

Things that caused me to feel this way:

____

____

____

____

____

Specifically, what thoughts did I have that led to me experiencing these emotions?

____

____

____

____

For the negative emotions, what thoughts or behaviors should I change or eliminate so that I will not feel these emotions when I have another experience similar to this:

____

____

____

____

What am I grateful for today?

____

____

____

____

Who/What made me laugh today?

____

Who showed me kindness today?

____

What did they do to demonstrate kindness to me?

____

____

____

____

Date: ____

Journal Entry (here is where can you discuss anything you'd like):

Day 54 Date: ______________________

The emotions that I experienced today are:

____

Things that caused me to feel this way:

____

____

____

____

Specifically, what thoughts did I have that led to me experiencing these emotions?

____

____

____

____

For the negative emotions, what thoughts or behaviors should I change or eliminate so that I will not feel these emotions when I have another experience similar to this:

____

____

____

____

What am I grateful for today?

____

____

____

____

Who/What made me laugh today?

____

Who showed me kindness today?

____

What did they do to demonstrate kindness to me?

____

____

____

____

Date: ______________________________

Journal Entry (here is where can you discuss anything you'd like):

Day 55 Date: ______________________________

The emotions that I experienced today are:

____

Things that caused me to feel this way:

____

____

____

____

Specifically, what thoughts did I have that led to me experiencing these emotions?

____

____

____

____

For the negative emotions, what thoughts or behaviors should I change or eliminate so that I will not feel these emotions when I have another experience similar to this:

____

____

____

____

What am I grateful for today?

____

____

____

____

Who/What made me laugh today?

____

Who showed me kindness today?

____

What did they do to demonstrate kindness to me?

____

____

____

____

Date: ____

Journal Entry (here is where can you discuss anything you'd like):

Day 56 Date:________________________

The emotions that I experienced today are:

Things that caused me to feel this way:

Specifically, what thoughts did I have that led to me experiencing these emotions?

For the negative emotions, what thoughts or behaviors should I change or eliminate so that I will not feel these emotions when I have another experience similar to this:

What am I grateful for today?

Who/What made me laugh today?

Who showed me kindness today?

____

What did they do to demonstrate kindness to me?

____

____

____

____

Date: ______________________________

Journal Entry (here is where can you discuss anything you'd like):

Snapshot of My Week

Check all of the positive traits that you demonstrated this week

Leadership
Kindness
Love
Loyalty
Humility
Compassion
Self-Compassion
Flexibility
Confidence
Teachable
Courage
Focus
Open Communication
Understanding
Selflessness
Authenticity
Fearlessness
Assertiveness
Self-Control
Forgiveness

Check all of the negative traits that you demonstrated this week

Anger
Malice
Judgement
Abrasive
Jealousy
Self-destructive
Envy
Stubborn
Rudeness
Gossip
Fear
Defensiveness
Deceit
Selfishness
Gullible
Manipulative

Best moment of the week

Worst moment of the week

Did I stay in control of my emotions this week?

Lessons learned

What do I need to change?

What can’t I change?

How can I move towards accepting what I can't change?

Day 57 Date: ______________________________

The emotions that I experienced today are:

____

Things that caused me to feel this way:

____
____
____
____

Specifically, what thoughts did I have that led to me experiencing these emotions?

____
____
____
____

For the negative emotions, what thoughts or behaviors should I change or eliminate so that I will not feel these emotions when I have another experience similar to this:

____
____
____
____

What am I grateful for today?

____
____
____
____

Who/What made me laugh today?

____

Who showed me kindness today?

____

What did they do to demonstrate kindness to me?

____

Date: ____

Journal Entry (here is where can you discuss anything you'd like):

Day 58 Date: ______________________________

The emotions that I experienced today are:

____

Things that caused me to feel this way:

____

____

____

____

Specifically, what thoughts did I have that led to me experiencing these emotions?

____

____

____

____

For the negative emotions, what thoughts or behaviors should I change or eliminate so that I will not feel these emotions when I have another experience similar to this:

____

____

____

____

What am I grateful for today?

____

____

____

____

Who/What made me laugh today?

____

Who showed me kindness today?

____

What did they do to demonstrate kindness to me?

____

____

____

____

Date: ______________________________

Journal Entry (here is where can you discuss anything you'd like):

Day 59 Date: ______________________

The emotions that I experienced today are:

____

Things that caused me to feel this way:

____

____

____

____

Specifically, what thoughts did I have that led to me experiencing these emotions?

____

____

____

____

For the negative emotions, what thoughts or behaviors should I change or eliminate so that I will not feel these emotions when I have another experience similar to this:

____

____

____

____

What am I grateful for today?

____

____

____

____

Who/What made me laugh today?

____

Who showed me kindness today?

____

What did they do to demonstrate kindness to me?

____

____

____

____

Date: ______________________________

Journal Entry (here is where can you discuss anything you'd like):

Day 60 Date: ______________________________

The emotions that I experienced today are:

____

Things that caused me to feel this way:

____

____

____

____

Specifically, what thoughts did I have that led to me experiencing these emotions?

____

____

____

____

For the negative emotions, what thoughts or behaviors should I change or eliminate so that I will not feel these emotions when I have another experience similar to this:

____

____

____

____

What am I grateful for today?

____

____

____

____

Who/What made me laugh today?

____

Who showed me kindness today?

____

What did they do to demonstrate kindness to me?

____

____

____

____

Date: ____

Journal Entry (here is where can you discuss anything you'd like):

Day 61 Date: ________________

The emotions that I experienced today are:

____

Things that caused me to feel this way:

____

____

____

____

Specifically, what thoughts did I have that led to me experiencing these emotions?

____

____

____

____

For the negative emotions, what thoughts or behaviors should I change or eliminate so that I will not feel these emotions when I have another experience similar to this:

____

____

____

____

What am I grateful for today?

____

____

____

____

Who/What made me laugh today?

____

Who showed me kindness today?

____

What did they do to demonstrate kindness to me?

____

____

____

____

Date: ____

Journal Entry (here is where can you discuss anything you'd like):

Day 62 Date: ______________________________

The emotions that I experienced today are:

____

Things that caused me to feel this way:

____
____
____
____

Specifically, what thoughts did I have that led to me experiencing these emotions?

____
____
____
____

For the negative emotions, what thoughts or behaviors should I change or eliminate so that I will not feel these emotions when I have another experience similar to this:

____
____
____
____

What am I grateful for today?

____
____
____
____

Who/What made me laugh today?

____

Who showed me kindness today?

____

What did they do to demonstrate kindness to me?

Date: ____

Journal Entry (here is where can you discuss anything you'd like):

Day 63 Date: ______________________

The emotions that I experienced today are:

____

Things that caused me to feel this way:

____

____

____

____

Specifically, what thoughts did I have that led to me experiencing these emotions?

____

____

____

____

For the negative emotions, what thoughts or behaviors should I change or eliminate so that I will not feel these emotions when I have another experience similar to this:

____

____

____

____

What am I grateful for today?

____

____

____

____

Who/What made me laugh today?

____

Who showed me kindness today?

____

What did they do to demonstrate kindness to me?

___

___

___

___

Date: ____

Journal Entry (here is where can you discuss anything you'd like):

Snapshot of My Week

Check all of the positive traits that you demonstrated this week

Leadership
Kindness
Love
Loyalty
Humility
Compassion
Self-Compassion
Flexibility
Confidence
Teachable
Courage
Focus
Open Communication
Understanding
Selflessness
Authenticity
Fearlessness
Assertiveness
Self-Control
Forgiveness

Check all of the negative traits that you demonstrated this week

Anger
Malice
Judgement
Abrasive
Jealousy
Self-destructive
Envy
Stubborn
Rudeness
Gossip
Fear
Defensiveness
Deceit
Selfishness
Gullible
Manipulative

Best moment of the week

Worst moment of the week

Did I stay in control of my emotions this week?

Lessons learned

What do I need to change?

What can't I change?

How can I move towards accepting what I can't change?

Day 64 Date: ______________________________

The emotions that I experienced today are:

____

Things that caused me to feel this way:

____
____
____
____

Specifically, what thoughts did I have that led to me experiencing these emotions?

____
____
____
____

For the negative emotions, what thoughts or behaviors should I change or eliminate so that I will not feel these emotions when I have another experience similar to this:

____
____
____
____

What am I grateful for today?

____
____
____
____

Who/What made me laugh today?

____

Who showed me kindness today?

____

What did they do to demonstrate kindness to me?

____

____

____

____

Date: ____

Journal Entry (here is where can you discuss anything you'd like):

Day 65 Date: ______________________

The emotions that I experienced today are:

____

Things that caused me to feel this way:

____

____

____

____

Specifically, what thoughts did I have that led to me experiencing these emotions?

____

____

____

____

For the negative emotions, what thoughts or behaviors should I change or eliminate so that I will not feel these emotions when I have another experience similar to this:

____

____

____

____

What am I grateful for today?

____

____

____

____

Who/What made me laugh today?

____

Who showed me kindness today?

____

What did they do to demonstrate kindness to me?

____

____

____

____

Date: ______________________________

Journal Entry (here is where can you discuss anything you'd like):

Day 66 Date: ______________________________

The emotions that I experienced today are:

____

Things that caused me to feel this way:

____

____

____

____

Specifically, what thoughts did I have that led to me experiencing these emotions?

____

____

____

____

For the negative emotions, what thoughts or behaviors should I change or eliminate so that I will not feel these emotions when I have another experience similar to this:

____

____

____

____

What am I grateful for today?

____

____

____

____

Who/What made me laugh today?

____

Who showed me kindness today?

____

What did they do to demonstrate kindness to me?

____

____

____

____

Date: ____________________

Journal Entry (here is where can you discuss anything you'd like):

Day 67 Date: ______________________________

The emotions that I experienced today are:

____

Things that caused me to feel this way:

____

____

____

____

Specifically, what thoughts did I have that led to me experiencing these emotions?

____

____

____

____

For the negative emotions, what thoughts or behaviors should I change or eliminate so that I will not feel these emotions when I have another experience similar to this:

____

____

____

____

What am I grateful for today?

____

____

____

____

Who/What made me laugh today?

____

Who showed me kindness today?

____

What did they do to demonstrate kindness to me?

____

____

____

____

Date: ______________________________

Journal Entry (here is where can you discuss anything you'd like):

Day 68 Date: ______________________

The emotions that I experienced today are:

____

Things that caused me to feel this way:

____

____

____

____

Specifically, what thoughts did I have that led to me experiencing these emotions?

____

____

____

____

For the negative emotions, what thoughts or behaviors should I change or eliminate so that I will not feel these emotions when I have another experience similar to this:

____

____

____

____

What am I grateful for today?

____

____

____

____

Who/What made me laugh today?

____

Who showed me kindness today?

____

What did they do to demonstrate kindness to me?

Date: ____________________

Journal Entry (here is where can you discuss anything you'd like):

Day 69 Date: ______________________________

The emotions that I experienced today are:

____

Things that caused me to feel this way:

____
____
____
____

Specifically, what thoughts did I have that led to me experiencing these emotions?

____
____
____
____

For the negative emotions, what thoughts or behaviors should I change or eliminate so that I will not feel these emotions when I have another experience similar to this:

____
____
____
____

What am I grateful for today?

____
____
____
____

Who/What made me laugh today?

____

Who showed me kindness today?

____

What did they do to demonstrate kindness to me?

____

____

____

____

Date: ______________________________

Journal Entry (here is where can you discuss anything you'd like):

Day 70 Date: ______________________

The emotions that I experienced today are:

____

Things that caused me to feel this way:

____

____

____

____

Specifically, what thoughts did I have that led to me experiencing these emotions?

____

____

____

____

For the negative emotions, what thoughts or behaviors should I change or eliminate so that I will not feel these emotions when I have another experience similar to this:

____

____

____

____

What am I grateful for today?

____

____

____

____

Who/What made me laugh today?

____

Who showed me kindness today?

____

What did they do to demonstrate kindness to me?

____

____

____

____

Date: ____________________

Journal Entry (here is where can you discuss anything you'd like):

Snapshot of My Week

Check all of the positive traits that you demonstrated this week

Leadership
Kindness
Love
Loyalty
Humility
Compassion
Self-Compassion
Flexibility
Confidence
Teachable
Courage
Focus
Open Communication
Understanding
Selflessness
Authenticity
Fearlessness
Assertiveness
Self-Control
Forgiveness

Check all of the negative traits that you demonstrated this week

Anger
Malice
Judgement
Abrasive
Jealousy
Self-destructive
Envy
Stubborn
Rudeness
Gossip
Fear
Defensiveness
Deceit
Selfishness
Gullible
Manipulative

Best moment of the week

Worst moment of the week

Did I stay in control of my emotions this week?

Lessons learned

What do I need to change?

What can't I change?

How can I move towards accepting what I can't change?

Monthly Goals Achieved

Monthly financial goals achieved

____
____
____
____
____
____

Monthly emotional goals achieved

____
____
____
____
____
____

Monthly nutrition goals achieved

____
____
____
____
____
____

Monthly professional goals achieved

____
____
____
____
____
____

Financial goals for the month

____
____
____
____
____
____

Emotional goals for the month

____
____
____
____
____
____

What trends or patterns have you noticed regarding your triggers?

Monthly Goals

Healthy eating goals for the month

Professional goals for the month

Exercise goals for the month

Monthly exercise goals achieved

Monthly prayers answered

Prayer requests for the month

Day 71 Date: ______________________________

The emotions that I experienced today are:

____

Things that caused me to feel this way:

____
____
____
____

Specifically, what thoughts did I have that led to me experiencing these emotions?

____
____
____
____

For the negative emotions, what thoughts or behaviors should I change or eliminate so that I will not feel these emotions when I have another experience similar to this:

____
____
____
____

What am I grateful for today?

____
____
____
____
____

Who/What made me laugh today?

____

Who showed me kindness today?

____

What did they do to demonstrate kindness to me?

____

____

____

____

Date: ______________________________

Journal Entry (here is where can you discuss anything you'd like):

Day 72

Date: ______________________________

The emotions that I experienced today are:

____

Things that caused me to feel this way:

____
____
____
____

Specifically, what thoughts did I have that led to me experiencing these emotions?

____
____
____
____

For the negative emotions, what thoughts or behaviors should I change or eliminate so that I will not feel these emotions when I have another experience similar to this:

____
____
____
____

What am I grateful for today?

____
____
____
____

Who/What made me laugh today?

____

Who showed me kindness today?

____

What did they do to demonstrate kindness to me?

____

____

____

____

Date: ____

Journal Entry (here is where can you discuss anything you'd like):

Day 73 Date: ___________________________

The emotions that I experienced today are:

___

Things that caused me to feel this way:

___

___

___

___

Specifically, what thoughts did I have that led to me experiencing these emotions?

___

___

___

___

For the negative emotions, what thoughts or behaviors should I change or eliminate so that I will not feel these emotions when I have another experience similar to this:

___

___

___

___

What am I grateful for today?

___

___

___

___

Who/What made me laugh today?

___

Who showed me kindness today?

___

What did they do to demonstrate kindness to me?

Date: ______________________________________

Journal Entry (here is where can you discuss anything you'd like):

Day 74 Date: ______________________

The emotions that I experienced today are:

____

Things that caused me to feel this way:

____

____

____

____

Specifically, what thoughts did I have that led to me experiencing these emotions?

____

____

____

____

For the negative emotions, what thoughts or behaviors should I change or eliminate so that I will not feel these emotions when I have another experience similar to this:

____

____

____

____

What am I grateful for today?

____

____

____

____

Who/What made me laugh today?

____

Who showed me kindness today?

____

What did they do to demonstrate kindness to me?

____

____

____

____

Date: ____

Journal Entry (here is where can you discuss anything you'd like):

Day 75 Date: ______________________________

The emotions that I experienced today are:

____

Things that caused me to feel this way:

____

____

____

____

Specifically, what thoughts did I have that led to me experiencing these emotions?

____

____

____

____

For the negative emotions, what thoughts or behaviors should I change or eliminate so that I will not feel these emotions when I have another experience similar to this:

____

____

____

____

What am I grateful for today?

____

____

____

____

Who/What made me laugh today?

____

Who showed me kindness today?

____

What did they do to demonstrate kindness to me?

____

____

____

____

Date: ____

Journal Entry (here is where can you discuss anything you'd like):

Day 76 Date: ______________________________

The emotions that I experienced today are:

____

Things that caused me to feel this way:

____

____

____

____

Specifically, what thoughts did I have that led to me experiencing these emotions?

____

____

____

____

For the negative emotions, what thoughts or behaviors should I change or eliminate so that I will not feel these emotions when I have another experience similar to this:

____

____

____

____

What am I grateful for today?

____

____

____

____

Who/What made me laugh today?

____

Who showed me kindness today?

____

What did they do to demonstrate kindness to me?

Date: ____

Journal Entry (here is where can you discuss anything you'd like):

Day 77

Date: ____________________

The emotions that I experienced today are:

____

Things that caused me to feel this way:

____

____

____

____

Specifically, what thoughts did I have that led to me experiencing these emotions?

____

____

____

____

For the negative emotions, what thoughts or behaviors should I change or eliminate so that I will not feel these emotions when I have another experience similar to this:

____

____

____

____

What am I grateful for today?

____

____

____

____

Who/What made me laugh today?

____

Who showed me kindness today?

____

What did they do to demonstrate kindness to me?

____

____

____

____

Date: ____

Journal Entry (here is where can you discuss anything you'd like):

Snapshot of My Week

Check all of the positive traits that you demonstrated this week

Leadership
Kindness
Love
Loyalty
Humility
Compassion
Self-Compassion
Flexibility
Confidence
Teachable
Courage
Focus
Open Communication
Understanding
Selflessness
Authenticity
Fearlessness
Assertiveness
Self-Control
Forgiveness

Check all of the negative traits that you demonstrated this week

Anger
Malice
Judgement
Abrasive
Jealousy
Self-destructive
Envy
Stubborn
Rudeness
Gossip
Fear
Defensiveness
Deceit
Selfishness
Gullible
Manipulative

Best moment of the week

Worst moment of the week

Did I stay in control of my emotions this week? How so?

Lessons learned

What do I need to change?

What can't I change?

How can I move towards accepting what I can't change?

Day 78 Date: ____________________________

The emotions that I experienced today are:

Things that caused me to feel this way:

Specifically, what thoughts did I have that led to me experiencing these emotions?

For the negative emotions, what thoughts or behaviors should I change or eliminate so that I will not feel these emotions when I have another experience similar to this:

What am I grateful for today?

Who/What made me laugh today?

Who showed me kindness today?

What did they do to demonstrate kindness to me?

____

____

____

____

Date: ____________________

Journal Entry (here is where can you discuss anything you'd like):

Day 79 Date: ______________________

The emotions that I experienced today are:

____

Things that caused me to feel this way:

____

____

____

____

Specifically, what thoughts did I have that led to me experiencing these emotions?

____

____

____

____

For the negative emotions, what thoughts or behaviors should I change or eliminate so that I will not feel these emotions when I have another experience similar to this:

____

____

____

____

What am I grateful for today?

____

____

____

____

Who/What made me laugh today?

____

Who showed me kindness today?

____

What did they do to demonstrate kindness to me?

____

____

____

____

Date: ____

Journal Entry (here is where can you discuss anything you'd like):

Day 80 Date: ______________________________

The emotions that I experienced today are:

____

Things that caused me to feel this way:

____

____

____

____

Specifically, what thoughts did I have that led to me experiencing these emotions?

____

____

____

____

For the negative emotions, what thoughts or behaviors should I change or eliminate so that I will not feel these emotions when I have another experience similar to this:

____

____

____

____

What am I grateful for today?

____

____

____

____

Who/What made me laugh today?

____

Who showed me kindness today?

____

What did they do to demonstrate kindness to me?

___

___

___

___

Date: ____

Journal Entry (here is where can you discuss anything you'd like):

Day 81 Date: ______________________

The emotions that I experienced today are:

____

Things that caused me to feel this way:

____
____
____
____

Specifically, what thoughts did I have that led to me experiencing these emotions?

____
____
____
____

For the negative emotions, what thoughts or behaviors should I change or eliminate so that I will not feel these emotions when I have another experience similar to this:

____
____
____
____

What am I grateful for today?

____
____
____
____

Who/What made me laugh today?

____

Who showed me kindness today?

____

What did they do to demonstrate kindness to me?

____

____

____

____

Date: ____

Journal Entry (here is where can you discuss anything you'd like):

Day 82 Date: ______________________________

The emotions that I experienced today are:

____

Things that caused me to feel this way:

____

____

____

____

Specifically, what thoughts did I have that led to me experiencing these emotions?

____

____

____

____

For the negative emotions, what thoughts or behaviors should I change or eliminate so that I will not feel these emotions when I have another experience similar to this:

____

____

____

____

What am I grateful for today?

____

____

____

____

Who/What made me laugh today?

____

Who showed me kindness today?

____

What did they do to demonstrate kindness to me?

____

____

____

____

Date: ____

Journal Entry (here is where can you discuss anything you'd like):

Day 83 Date: ______________________

The emotions that I experienced today are:

____

Things that caused me to feel this way:

____

____

____

____

Specifically, what thoughts did I have that led to me experiencing these emotions?

____

____

____

____

For the negative emotions, what thoughts or behaviors should I change or eliminate so that I will not feel these emotions when I have another experience similar to this:

____

____

____

____

What am I grateful for today?

____

____

____

____

Who/What made me laugh today?

____

Who showed me kindness today?

____

What did they do to demonstrate kindness to me?

Date: ______________________________

Journal Entry (here is where can you discuss anything you'd like):

Day 84 Date: ________________________________

The emotions that I experienced today are:

____

Things that caused me to feel this way:

____

____

____

____

Specifically, what thoughts did I have that led to me experiencing these emotions?

____

____

____

____

For the negative emotions, what thoughts or behaviors should I change or eliminate so that I will not feel these emotions when I have another experience similar to this:

____

____

____

____

What am I grateful for today?

____

____

____

____

Who/What made me laugh today?

____

Who showed me kindness today?

____

What did they do to demonstrate kindness to me?

____

____

____

____

Date: ______________________________________

Journal Entry (here is where can you discuss anything you'd like):

Snapshot of My Week

Check all of the positive traits that you demonstrated this week

Leadership
Kindness
Love
Loyalty
Humility
Compassion
Self-Compassion
Flexibility
Confidence
Teachable
Courage
Focus
Open Communication
Understanding
Selflessness
Authenticity
Fearlessness
Assertiveness
Self-Control
Forgiveness

Check all of the negative traits that you demonstrated this week

Anger
Malice
Judgement
Abrasive
Jealousy
Self-destructive
Envy
Stubborn
Rudeness
Gossip
Fear
Defensiveness
Deceit
Selfishness
Gullible
Manipulative

Best moment of the week

Worst moment of the week

Did I stay in control of my emotions this week?

Lessons learned

What do I need to change?

What can't I change?

How can I move towards accepting what I can't change?

Day 85 Date: ______________________

The emotions that I experienced today are:

____

Things that caused me to feel this way:

____
____
____
____
____

Specifically, what thoughts did I have that led to me experiencing these emotions?

____
____
____
____
____

For the negative emotions, what thoughts or behaviors should I change or eliminate so that I will not feel these emotions when I have another experience similar to this:

____
____
____
____

What am I grateful for today?

____
____
____
____

Who/What made me laugh today?

____

Who showed me kindness today?

____

What did they do to demonstrate kindness to me?

____

____

____

____

Date: ______________________________

Journal Entry (here is where can you discuss anything you'd like):

Day 86 Date: ______________________________

The emotions that I experienced today are:

____

Things that caused me to feel this way:

____
____
____
____

Specifically, what thoughts did I have that led to me experiencing these emotions?

____
____
____
____

For the negative emotions, what thoughts or behaviors should I change or eliminate so that I will not feel these emotions when I have another experience similar to this:

____
____
____
____

What am I grateful for today?

____
____
____
____
____

Who/What made me laugh today?

____

Who showed me kindness today?

____

What did they do to demonstrate kindness to me?

___

___

___

___

Date: ____

Journal Entry (here is where can you discuss anything you'd like):

Day 87 Date: ______________________________

The emotions that I experienced today are:

____

Things that caused me to feel this way:

____
____
____
____

Specifically, what thoughts did I have that led to me experiencing these emotions?

____
____
____
____

For the negative emotions, what thoughts or behaviors should I change or eliminate so that I will not feel these emotions when I have another experience similar to this:

____
____
____
____

What am I grateful for today?

____
____
____
____

Who/What made me laugh today?

____

Who showed me kindness today?

____

What did they do to demonstrate kindness to me?

____

____

____

____

Date: ____

Journal Entry (here is where can you discuss anything you'd like):

Day 88

Date: ______________________________

The emotions that I experienced today are:

____

Things that caused me to feel this way:

____

____

____

____

____

Specifically, what thoughts did I have that led to me experiencing these emotions?

____

____

____

____

For the negative emotions, what thoughts or behaviors should I change or eliminate so that I will not feel these emotions when I have another experience similar to this:

____

____

____

____

What am I grateful for today?

____

____

____

____

Who/What made me laugh today?

____

Who showed me kindness today?

____

What did they do to demonstrate kindness to me?

Date: ____

Journal Entry (here is where can you discuss anything you'd like):

Day 89 Date: ______________________

The emotions that I experienced today are:

____

Things that caused me to feel this way:

____

____

____

____

Specifically, what thoughts did I have that led to me experiencing these emotions?

____

____

____

____

For the negative emotions, what thoughts or behaviors should I change or eliminate so that I will not feel these emotions when I have another experience similar to this:

____

____

____

____

What am I grateful for today?

____

____

____

____

Who/What made me laugh today?

____

Who showed me kindness today?

____

What did they do to demonstrate kindness to me?

Date: ____________________

Journal Entry (here is where can you discuss anything you'd like):

Day 90 Date: ______________________________

The emotions that I experienced today are:

____

Things that caused me to feel this way:

____

____

____

____

Specifically, what thoughts did I have that led to me experiencing these emotions?

____

____

____

____

For the negative emotions, what thoughts or behaviors should I change or eliminate so that I will not feel these emotions when I have another experience similar to this:

____

____

____

____

What am I grateful for today?

____

____

____

____

Who/What made me laugh today?

____

Who showed me kindness today?

____

What did they do to demonstrate kindness to me?

____

____

____

____

Date: ____

Journal Entry (here is where can you discuss anything you'd like):

Day 91 Date: ______________________________

The emotions that I experienced today are:

____

Things that caused me to feel this way:

____
____
____
____
____

Specifically, what thoughts did I have that led to me experiencing these emotions?

____
____
____
____
____

For the negative emotions, what thoughts or behaviors should I change or eliminate so that I will not feel these emotions when I have another experience similar to this:

____
____
____
____

What am I grateful for today?

____
____
____
____

Who/What made me laugh today?

____

Who showed me kindness today?

____

What did they do to demonstrate kindness to me?

___

___

___

___

Date: ____

Journal Entry (here is where can you discuss anything you'd like):

Snapshot of My Week

Check all of the positive traits that you demonstrated this week

Leadership
Kindness
Love
Loyalty
Humility
Compassion
Self-Compassion
Flexibility
Confidence
Teachable
Courage
Focus
Open Communication
Understanding
Selflessness
Authenticity
Fearlessness
Assertiveness
Self-Control
Forgiveness

Check all of the negative traits that you demonstrated this week

Anger
Malice
Judgement
Abrasive
Jealousy
Self-destructive
Envy
Stubborn
Rudeness
Gossip
Fear
Defensiveness
Deceit
Selfishness
Gullible
Manipulative

Best moment of the week

Worst moment of the week

Did I stay in control of my emotions this week?

Lessons learned

What do I need to change?

What can't I change?

How can I move towards accepting what I can't change?

Day 92 Date: ______________________________

The emotions that I experienced today are:

____

Things that caused me to feel this way:

____

____

____

____

Specifically, what thoughts did I have that led to me experiencing these emotions?

____

____

____

____

For the negative emotions, what thoughts or behaviors should I change or eliminate so that I will not feel these emotions when I have another experience similar to this:

____

____

____

____

What am I grateful for today?

____

____

____

____

Who/What made me laugh today?

____

Who showed me kindness today?

____

What did they do to demonstrate kindness to me?

____

____

____

____

Date: ______________________________________

Journal Entry (here is where can you discuss anything you'd like):

Day 93 Date: ______________________________

The emotions that I experienced today are:

____

Things that caused me to feel this way:

____

____

____

____

Specifically, what thoughts did I have that led to me experiencing these emotions?

____

____

____

____

For the negative emotions, what thoughts or behaviors should I change or eliminate so that I will not feel these emotions when I have another experience similar to this:

____

____

____

____

What am I grateful for today?

____

____

____

____

Who/What made me laugh today?

____

Who showed me kindness today?

____

What did they do to demonstrate kindness to me?

Date: ____________________

Journal Entry (here is where can you discuss anything you'd like):

Day 94 Date: ______________________________

The emotions that I experienced today are:

____

Things that caused me to feel this way:

____
____
____
____

Specifically, what thoughts did I have that led to me experiencing these emotions?

____
____
____
____

For the negative emotions, what thoughts or behaviors should I change or eliminate so that I will not feel these emotions when I have another experience similar to this:

____
____
____
____

What am I grateful for today?

____
____
____
____

Who/What made me laugh today?

____

Who showed me kindness today?

____

What did they do to demonstrate kindness to me?

____

____

____

____

Date: ____

Journal Entry (here is where can you discuss anything you'd like):

Day 95

Date: ______________________________

The emotions that I experienced today are:

____

Things that caused me to feel this way:

____

____

____

____

Specifically, what thoughts did I have that led to me experiencing these emotions?

____

____

____

____

For the negative emotions, what thoughts or behaviors should I change or eliminate so that I will not feel these emotions when I have another experience similar to this:

____

____

____

____

What am I grateful for today?

____

____

____

____

Who/What made me laugh today?

____

Who showed me kindness today?

____

What did they do to demonstrate kindness to me?

____

____

____

____

Date: ____________________

Journal Entry (here is where can you discuss anything you'd like):

Day 96 Date: ____________________

The emotions that I experienced today are:

____

Things that caused me to feel this way:

____

____

____

____

Specifically, what thoughts did I have that led to me experiencing these emotions?

____

____

____

____

For the negative emotions, what thoughts or behaviors should I change or eliminate so that I will not feel these emotions when I have another experience similar to this:

____

____

____

____

What am I grateful for today?

____

____

____

____

Who/What made me laugh today?

____

Who showed me kindness today?

____

What did they do to demonstrate kindness to me?

____

____

____

____

Date: ______________________________

Journal Entry (here is where can you discuss anything you'd like):

Day 97 Date: ______________________

The emotions that I experienced today are:

____

Things that caused me to feel this way:

____

____

____

____

Specifically, what thoughts did I have that led to me experiencing these emotions?

____

____

____

____

For the negative emotions, what thoughts or behaviors should I change or eliminate so that I will not feel these emotions when I have another experience similar to this:

____

____

____

____

What am I grateful for today?

____

____

____

____

Who/What made me laugh today?

____

Who showed me kindness today?

____

What did they do to demonstrate kindness to me?

___

___

___

___

Date: ______________________________

Journal Entry (here is where can you discuss anything you'd like):

Day 98

Date: ______________________________

The emotions that I experienced today are:

____

Things that caused me to feel this way:

____

____

____

____

Specifically, what thoughts did I have that led to me experiencing these emotions?

____

____

____

____

For the negative emotions, what thoughts or behaviors should I change or eliminate so that I will not feel these emotions when I have another experience similar to this:

____

____

____

____

What am I grateful for today?

____

____

____

____

Who/What made me laugh today?

____

Who showed me kindness today?

____

What did they do to demonstrate kindness to me?

____

____

____

____

Date: ___________________________________

Journal Entry (here is where can you discuss anything you'd like):

Snapshot of My Week

Check all of the positive traits that you demonstrated this week

Leadership
Kindness
Love
Loyalty
Humility
Compassion
Self-Compassion
Flexibility
Confidence
Teachable
Courage
Focus
Open Communication
Understanding
Selflessness
Authenticity
Fearlessness
Assertiveness
Self-Control
Forgiveness

Check all of the negative traits that you demonstrated this week

Anger
Malice
Judgement
Abrasive
Jealousy
Self-destructive
Envy
Stubborn
Rudeness
Gossip
Fear
Defensiveness
Deceit
Selfishness
Gullible
Manipulative

Best moment of the week

Worst moment of the week

Did I stay in control of my emotions this week?

Lessons learned

What do I need to change?

What can't I change?

How can I move towards accepting what I can't change?

Day 99 Date: ______________________

The emotions that I experienced today are:

____

Things that caused me to feel this way:

____
____
____
____

Specifically, what thoughts did I have that led to me experiencing these emotions?

____
____
____
____

For the negative emotions, what thoughts or behaviors should I change or eliminate so that I will not feel these emotions when I have another experience similar to this:

____
____
____
____

What am I grateful for today?

____
____
____
____

Who/What made me laugh today?

____

Who showed me kindness today?

____

What did they do to demonstrate kindness to me?

____

____

____

____

Date: ______________________________________

Journal Entry (here is where can you discuss anything you'd like):

Day 100 Date: ____________________

The emotions that I experienced today are:

____

Things that caused me to feel this way:

____

____

____

____

Specifically, what thoughts did I have that led to me experiencing these emotions?

____

____

____

____

For the negative emotions, what thoughts or behaviors should I change or eliminate so that I will not feel these emotions when I have another experience similar to this:

____

____

____

____

What am I grateful for today?

____

____

____

____

Who/What made me laugh today?

____

Who showed me kindness today?

____

What did they do to demonstrate kindness to me?

___

___

___

___

Date: ____

Journal Entry (here is where can you discuss anything you'd like):

Day 101 Date: ______________________________

The emotions that I experienced today are:

____

Things that caused me to feel this way:

____
____
____
____

Specifically, what thoughts did I have that led to me experiencing these emotions?

____
____
____
____

For the negative emotions, what thoughts or behaviors should I change or eliminate so that I will not feel these emotions when I have another experience similar to this:

____
____
____
____

What am I grateful for today?

____
____
____
____

Who/What made me laugh today?

____

Who showed me kindness today?

____

What did they do to demonstrate kindness to me?

____

____

____

____

Date: ____

Journal Entry (here is where can you discuss anything you'd like):

Day 102 Date: ____________________

The emotions that I experienced today are:

____

Things that caused me to feel this way:

____
____
____
____

Specifically, what thoughts did I have that led to me experiencing these emotions?

____
____
____
____

For the negative emotions, what thoughts or behaviors should I change or eliminate so that I will not feel these emotions when I have another experience similar to this:

____
____
____
____

What am I grateful for today?

____
____
____
____

Who/What made me laugh today?

____

Who showed me kindness today?

____

What did they do to demonstrate kindness to me?

___

___

___

___

Date: ____

Journal Entry (here is where can you discuss anything you'd like):

Day 103 Date: ______________________

The emotions that I experienced today are:

____

Things that caused me to feel this way:

____
____
____
____

Specifically, what thoughts did I have that led to me experiencing these emotions?

____
____
____
____

For the negative emotions, what thoughts or behaviors should I change or eliminate so that I will not feel these emotions when I have another experience similar to this:

____
____
____
____

What am I grateful for today?

____
____
____
____

Who/What made me laugh today?

____

Who showed me kindness today?

____

What did they do to demonstrate kindness to me?

Date: ____________________________________

Journal Entry (here is where can you discuss anything you'd like):

Day 104 Date: ______________________________

The emotions that I experienced today are:

____

Things that caused me to feel this way:

____
____
____
____

Specifically, what thoughts did I have that led to me experiencing these emotions?

____
____
____
____

For the negative emotions, what thoughts or behaviors should I change or eliminate so that I will not feel these emotions when I have another experience similar to this:

____
____
____
____

What am I grateful for today?

____
____
____
____

Who/What made me laugh today?

____

Who showed me kindness today?

____

What did they do to demonstrate kindness to me?

____

____

____

____

Date: ____

Journal Entry (here is where can you discuss anything you'd like):

Day 105 Date: ____________________

The emotions that I experienced today are:

___

Things that caused me to feel this way:

___

___

___

___

Specifically, what thoughts did I have that led to me experiencing these emotions?

___

___

___

___

For the negative emotions, what thoughts or behaviors should I change or eliminate so that I will not feel these emotions when I have another experience similar to this:

___

___

___

___

What am I grateful for today?

___

___

___

___

Who/What made me laugh today?

___

Who showed me kindness today?

___

What did they do to demonstrate kindness to me?

____

____

____

____

Date: ____

Journal Entry (here is where can you discuss anything you'd like):

Snapshot of My Week

Check all of the positive traits that you demonstrated this week

- Leadership
- Kindness
- Love
- Loyalty
- Humility
- Compassion
- Self-Compassion
- Flexibility
- Confidence
- Teachable
- Courage
- Focus
- Open Communication
- Understanding
- Selflessness
- Authenticity
- Fearlessness
- Assertiveness
- Self-Control
- Forgiveness

Check all of the negative traits that you demonstrated this week

- Anger
- Malice
- Judgement
- Abrasive
- Jealousy
- Self-destructive
- Envy
- Stubborn
- Rudeness
- Gossip
- Fear
- Defensiveness
- Deceit
- Selfishness
- Gullible
- Manipulative

Best moment of the week

Worst moment of the week

Did I stay in control of my emotions this week?

Lessons learned

What do I need to change?

What can't I change?

How can I move towards accepting what I can't change?

Monthly Goals Achieved

Monthly financial goals achieved

____
____
____
____
____
____

Monthly emotional goals achieved

____
____
____
____
____
____

Monthly nutrition goals achieved

____
____
____
____
____
____

Monthly professional goals achieved

____
____
____
____
____
____

Monthly exercise goals achieved

____
____
____
____
____
____

Monthly prayers answered

____
____
____
____
____
____
____

Notes

1. Ackerman, Courtney. (10 October 2020). *83 Benefits for Journaling for Depression, Anxiety, and Stress*. https://positivepsychology.com/benefits-of-journaling/
2. Nguyen, Thai. (13 Feb 2015). *10 Surprising Benefits you will get from Keeping a Journal.* https://www.huffpost.com/entry/benefits-of-journaling-_b_6648884

Made in the USA
Middletown, DE
30 November 2021